GRAPHIC HISTORY

ROSA PARKS

AND THE Montgomery Bus Boycott

by Connie Colwell Miller
illustrated by Dan Kalal

Consultant:
Charles P. Henry,
Professor, African American Studies
University of California, Berkeley

® **www.raintreepublishers.co.uk**
Visit our website to find out
more information about
Raintree books.

To order:
☎ Phone 0845 6044371
▤ Fax +44 (0) 1865 312263
▥ Email myorders@raintreepublishers.co.uk

Customers from outside the UK please telephone +44 1865 312262

Raintree is an imprint of Capstone Global Library Limited, a company incorporated in England and Wales having
its registered office at 7 Pilgrim Street, London, EC4V 6LB – Registered company number: 6695582

Text © Capstone Press 2007
First published in hardback in the United Kingdom by Capstone Global Library in 2011
The moral rights of the proprietor have been asserted.

Designer: Alison Thiele
Illustrator: Dan Kalal
Colourist: Michael Kelleher
Editors: Erika L. Shores and John-Paul Wilkins
Originated by Capstone Global Library
Printed and bound in China by South China Printing Company Ltd

ISBN 978 1 406 22556 3 (hardback)
15 14 13 12 11
10 9 8 7 6 5 4 3 2 1

British Library Cataloguing in Publication Data
Miller, Connie Colwell.
Rosa Parks and the Montgomery Bus Boycott. -- (Graphic history)
323.1'196073'092-dc22
A full catalogue record for this book is available from the British Library.

Editor's note: Direct quotations from primary sources are indicated by a yellow background.

Direct quotations appear on the following pages:
Pages 6, 7, 8, 9, 11 (top), 25, 26, from Douglas Brinkley's interviews with Rosa Parks as quoted
in *Rosa Parks*, Douglas Brinkley (Viking, 2000).
Page 11 (bottom), from *The Montgomery Bus Boycott and the Women Who Started It: The
Memoir of Jo Ann Gibson Robinson*, Jo Ann Gibson Robinson (University of Tennessee Press, 1987).
Page 21, from *The Autobiography of Martin Luther King Jr.* edited by Clayborne Carson
(Intellectual Properties Management in association with Warner Books, 1998).

CONTENTS

Chapter 1

ROSA TAKES A STAND

Rosa Parks was a young African-American woman living in Montgomery, Alabama, USA, in 1943. At the time, segregation laws kept blacks and whites apart in most places. African Americans like Rosa faced unfair treatment because of these laws.

You, get off my bus and board through the back door, where the blacks belong.

I'm already on the bus, and I've paid my fare. I see no need to reboard through the back door. People are waiting behind me.

If you won't board through the back, then you can't ride my bus.

Rosa refused to enter the bus through the back door. She got off and vowed never again to ride a bus driven by that man.

The bus driver turned around. Rosa had been too lost in her thoughts to notice him before.
And now she was staring right at the same bus driver who had ordered her off his bus 12 years earlier.
Move ya'll, I want those two seats!
Ya'll better make it light on yourselves and let me have those seats.

Rosa didn't want to be arrested. But she felt strongly that it was time to stop accepting the unfair treatment.
I'm a good person, and I always do what's right. It's not me who's wrong, it's this law.
You look like a nice lady. Why did you refuse to stand?
Why do you all push us around?
I don't know, but the law is the law, and you're under arrest.

Chapter 2

THE BUS BOYCOTT

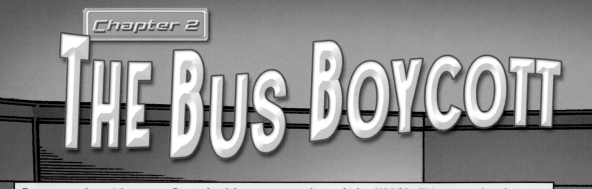

For more than 12 years, Rosa had been a member of the NAACP. This organization wanted fair treatment for African Americans. Edgar Nixon was a former president of Montgomery's NAACP. As a secretary for the NAACP, Rosa had worked with Nixon. The night of Rosa's arrest, Nixon met with her and her family.

We need to do something about the way blacks are treated in this community, and we need to do something now!

Rosa, we have to make your case public. We'll use it to spark a protest against segregation. If this law requires the arrest of a woman like you, it's proof that the law needs to change.

When Monday came, an amazing thing happened.

Will you look at that? The buses are almost empty!

Well, most of Montgomery's bus passengers are black. How will they manage to fill their buses without us?

Meanwhile, Rosa's case was heard in court.

I find the defendant, Rosa Parks, guilty of breaking the bus segregation law.

I expected this verdict. We'll appeal this case all the way to the Supreme Court if we have to.

Our appeals will draw the country's attention to Montgomery's segregation laws.

On the evening of 5 December, Montgomery's African-American community packed the Holt Street Baptist Church. They would vote to decide whether to continue the boycott.

We are here to say to those who have mistreated us that we are tired – tired of being segregated and humiliated. Democracy gives us the right to protest for our rights.

Overwhelmingly, they agreed to continue the bus boycott.

At least 30,000 African Americans refused to ride the Montgomery buses.

15

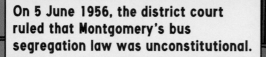

On 5 June 1956, the district court ruled that Montgomery's bus segregation law was unconstitutional.

This is what we have hoped for, Dr King.

We can't celebrate yet, Rosa. Montgomery city officials are sure to appeal the verdict to the US Supreme Court. We'll have to wait until their ruling before we can put an end to the bus segregation.

On 13 November 1956, the US Supreme Court finally ruled that bus segregation was illegal.

The universe is on the side of justice.

One month later, Montgomery buses were no longer segregated. The boycott had lasted 13 months.
Finally, our long wait for equality on public buses has come to an end.

Rosa and the MIA leaders had won a major victory.

We still have much work to do for civil rights, Dr King.

We will not rest until African Americans and whites are treated as equals!

Rosa was proud of what she had done, but the new law angered many white people. Rosa received death threats and frightening phone calls.

Rosa, it's time to move north to Detroit. We'll be treated better there.

The Montgomery bus boycott helped bring national attention to civil rights. The boycott launched Martin Luther King Jr as the voice of the movement. In the 1960s, Rosa continued to help King. She travelled to Washington, DC for the March on Washington.

I have a dream that one day on the red hills of Georgia, the sons of former slaves and the sons of former slaveholders will be able to sit down together at the table of brotherhood.

I have a dream that my four little children will one day live in a nation where they will not be judged by the colour of their skin but by the content of their character.

But peaceful protests in Alabama were sometimes met with violence. Rosa often travelled back to do whatever she could to help.

Of course I'll give my support to the marchers. I will be on the first plane there.

Rosa arrived in Montgomery to take part in a march to the state capital. King organized the march to protest against the violence.

We may have integrated the buses in Montgomery, but we have a long way to go before there will be peace between blacks and whites here.

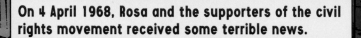

Chapter 4
LEAVING HER MARK

On 4 April 1968, Rosa and the supporters of the civil rights movement received some terrible news.

Peaceful protestor Dr Martin Luther King Jr has died of a gunshot wound.

Oh, Mother! We have lost our greatest leader!

Rosa kept her promise to continue working for civil rights.

We need to keep up the fight. Blacks everywhere need to be able to vote and be free from job discrimination. We can't stop until all the problems are fixed.

In 1977, Rosa's husband died. Three years later, her mother passed away.

Rosa became friends with a young woman named Elaine Eason Steele. Together, the two women created the Rosa and Raymond Parks Institute in 1987. This Detroit institute works to teach young people how to be good leaders.

This institute is my lifelong dream. I just love the young people; they're our angels of the future.

The institute organized bus tours called Freedom Rides for young people. These bus tours taught kids about historical events, such as the 1960s Freedom Rides.

In 1961, 13 people — some black, some white — rode from Washington, DC to New Orleans, Louisiana. They wanted to test the new law against segregation. My friends, those riders faced bombs and beatings.

Throughout her life, Rosa was often asked to speak about that important day in December 1955.

When I declined to give up my seat, it was not that day, or bus, in particular. I just wanted to be free like everybody else. I did not want to be continually humiliated over something I had no control over: the colour of my skin.

Rosa Parks died on 24 October 2005, at the age of 92. The woman who became known as the mother of the civil rights movement was honoured by people across the United States. She was the first woman in US history to lie in state at the US Capitol Rotunda. Thousands of mourners came to pay their respects to the woman who helped spark a movement by simply refusing to give up her seat on a bus.

More about
ROSA PARKS

Rosa Parks was born on 4 February 1913, in Alabama, USA. Her parents were James and Leona McCauley.

NAACP stands for the National Association for the Advancement of Colored People. It formed in the early 1900s. Rosa became a member in 1943.

A white supremacy group called the Ku Klux Klan (KKK) terrorized African Americans for many years. The KKK often beat and killed African Americans. When Rosa was young, she sat up late with her grandfather, guarding the house against KKK attacks.

Because she was so kind and gentle, many people thought that Rosa disapproved of using force in the fight for civil rights. In reality, Rosa believed that it was important to stand up for human rights, even if that meant sometimes using force.

Two women had refused to give up their bus seats before Rosa did in 1955. They were arrested, just like Rosa. But it was Rosa's character that made her the best person to represent black people in the fight for bus integration.

In 1956, Rosa posed for a photograph that soon became famous. She boarded a bus and a white reporter posed behind her. For many people, this image symbolized bus integration. The driver that day was the same driver who had her arrested the year before.

From 1987 to 2000, about 5,000 young people participated in activities at the Rosa and Raymond Parks Institute.

GLOSSARY

appeal ask for a decision made by a court of law to be changed

bail sum of money paid to a court to allow someone accused of a crime to be set free until his or her trial

boycott refuse to take part in something as a way of making a protest

integration act or practice of making public facilities open to people of all races and ethnic groups

lie in state public display of someone's coffin to allow people to pay their respects before the burial

March on Washington political rally in which 250,000 people gathered in Washington, DC to protest against the lack of civil rights for African Americans

segregation act or practice of keeping people apart because of their race

verdict decision of a jury on whether an accused person is guilty or not guilty

INTERNET SITES

www.bbc.co.uk/learningzone/clips/rosa-parks/5191.html
Visit this website to hear a radio clip of Rosa Parks explaining why she made her stand on that day in 1955.

http://www.historylearningsite.co.uk/civil1.htm
This website provides information about Rosa Parks and the Montgomery bus boycott, as well as other important figures and events in the civil rights movement.

READ MORE

The Bus Ride that Changed History: The Story of Rosa Parks, Pamela Duncan Edwards (Turtleback Books, 2009)

Rosa Parks: Civil Rights Pioneer (Time for Kids Biographies), Karen Kellaher (Collins, 2007)

Rosa Parks: The Life of a Civil Rights Heroine (Graphic Biographies), Rob Shone and Nick Spender (Franklin Watts, 2009)

The Story of Rosa Parks, Patricia A. Pingry (Ideals Publishing Corporation, 2007)

BIBLIOGRAPHY

Daybreak of Freedom: The Montogomery Bus Boycott, Stewart Burns (ed.) (The University of North Carolina Press, 1997)

The Montgomery Bus Boycott and the Women Who Started It: The Memoir of Jo Ann Gibson Robinson, Jo Ann Gibson Robinson (University of Tennessee Press, 1987)

My Story, Rosa Parks, with Jim Haskins (Dial Books, 1992)

Rosa Parks (Penguin Lives Series), Douglas Brinkley (Viking, 2000)

INDEX